STORIES FROM ANCIENT GREECE

Retold by Pamela Oldfield
Illustrated by Nick Harris

KINGFISHER BOOKS

For Wendy and Jane

Kingfisher Books, Grisewood & Dempsey Ltd.,
Elsley House, 24–30 Great Titchfield Street,
London W1P 7AD

First published in 1988 by Kingfisher Books

Reprinted 1989

BRITISH LIBRARY CATALOGUING IN PUBLICATION DATA
Oldfield, Pamela
Stories from Ancient Greece.
1. Mythology, Greek – Juvenile literature
I. Title II. Harris, Nick
292'.13   BL790
ISBN 0-86272-215-2

Edited by Sarah Elliot and Kate Hayden
Cover design by 20/20 Graphics
Phototypeset by SPAN (Southern Positives and Negatives)
Colour separations by Newsele Litho Spa, Milan
Printed in Italy

CONTENTS

PERSEPHONE
AND THE
KING OF DARKNESS

THERE was once a goddess whose name was Demeter. Demeter was welcomed wherever she went because she possessed wonderful powers. She made the flowers bloom, she made the corn ripen and she filled the trees with fruit. Everywhere she went she breathed life into the plants, and without her the world would have become a dreary, lifeless place.

Now Demeter had a daughter called Persephone, who grew as beautifully as any plant. Her body was as straight and supple as a young willow, and her skin as soft as a rose petal. Persephone and her mother could not bear to be parted so they travelled the world together to bring in the Earth's harvests. One day, while they were journeying through Sicily, Persephone wandered away from her mother to explore the green meadows around Mount Etna. She

9

began to pick the small white flowers that grew there. When she had gathered enough she sat down and began to make a circlet of flowers for her hair.

Little did she know that at that very moment, far below her in the darkness of the Earth, Hades was getting ready to ride out with his chariot and horses. Hades was the King of Darkness and he lived below the mountain in a gloomy place. Suddenly the ground beneath Persephone began to tremble.

The mountain split apart with a crashing of rocks and stones, and Persephone watched in amazement as Hades appeared in an ebony chariot drawn by four black horses. Hades was as dark as Persephone was fair. His eyes were like two dark coals in his swarthy face and his long black hair streamed out behind him. The horses galloped furiously across the mountainside. Persephone guessed at once who he was. Her one thought was to run back to her mother before he saw her but, as she ran, she stumbled and fell. She screamed for Demeter but only Hades heard her cry. He turned his chariot and rode back. As he stared down at the beautiful young woman he thought that if only he had a wife, he need never be lonely again.

"I am Hades, King of Darkness," he told her. "Who are you?"

"I am Persephone," she answered in a trembling voice. "My mother is the goddess Demeter."

The longer Hades looked at Persephone, the more he felt he could not live without her. But how could he ask such a radiant creature to share his life of darkness? She would never agree. Suddenly he leant down and pulled Persephone into his chariot and carried her down into his palace. The mountainside closed behind them and all that was left was the circlet of white flowers.

Days later Demeter found the flowers as she searched for her lost daughter. As soon as she saw them she knew that something terrible had happened. Frantically she continued her search, but no one could tell her what had taken place on the mountainside. Weeks went by and Demeter went on searching. She neglected her work and all over the world the crops began to fail. The corn would not ripen without her; fruit would not grow and all the flowers withered and died. People grew alarmed and appealed to Zeus, who was King over all the gods. Zeus sent at once for Demeter and asked her what was happening.

"My daughter has disappeared," she told him tearfully. "I cannot rest until I find her."

"I will send out my messengers," Zeus told her. "We shall find her, never fear."

Poor Demeter waited without much hope, but at last a messenger hurried back to Zeus with news.

"Persephone has been captured by the King of Darkness," he told them. "He has taken her to his underground palace below Mount Etna." At these words, Demeter's eyes filled with tears.

"I shall never see my daughter again," she wept. Zeus sent the messenger back to Hades to demand an explanation. Hades could not refuse a messenger from Zeus, so he agreed to see him.

"Tell your master I mean Persephone no harm," Hades insisted. "I want to make her my wife. She will be the Queen of Darkness, and I will love her for ever." Persephone looked up at him and shook her head sadly.

"I can never agree to marry you," she said. "I could never be happy in such a gloomy place, and I long to see my mother again. If you keep me here against my will, I shall die."

12

The messenger returned and explained the situation to Zeus while Demeter listened anxiously. She knew that if Zeus could not rescue her daughter no one could. Zeus thought long and hard. At last he looked up. There was a gleam in his eye and Demeter was suddenly hopeful.

"Go back to Hades," Zeus commanded the messenger, "and ask if Persephone has eaten anything since she entered the palace. If not, Hades cannot keep her against her will and we shall be able to save her." For Zeus knew that anyone who has shared food with Hades in his underground kingdom must remain there for ever.

Meanwhile Hades was growing worried about Persephone because she had eaten nothing and was looking pale and thin.

"I must tempt her to eat," he said to himself. "If she doesn't eat she will die. I want to make her happy so that she will *want* to stay with me. Perhaps she would accept a pomegranate."

"Dear Persephone," he said gently. "Please try to eat a little of this pomegranate. I cannot bear to see you like this. It is breaking my heart." Persephone felt sorry for him, and to please him she took six seeds from the pomegranate and put them into her mouth. As she did so the messenger from Zeus burst into the room.

"Do not eat that fruit, Persephone!" he cried. "If you have eaten nothing since you came here Zeus can save you!"

"I have eaten six seeds," she stammered. Hades was so relieved he took her in his arms and kissed her. Now no one could take her from him.

"Now you must stay with me for ever," he told her. "Marry me, Persephone. You shall be the Queen of Darkness and I swear I shall make you happy."

But still Persephone shook her head. When the messenger told

Zeus about the pomegranate seeds he was very worried. If Persephone stayed with Hades, Demeter would lose interest in everything. She would sit at home, sighing over her loss. Plants would die and all over the world people would starve.

"We must find a way to save Persephone," said Zeus. "If we don't, the grass and trees will disappear from the Earth and it will become a desert. I must find a way to bring mother and daughter together again."

At last he had an idea. This time he went to Hades himself.

"I know Persephone has eaten six pomegranate seeds," said Zeus, "but if you really love Persephone you will want to make her happy. I suggest that she stays here with you as your wife for six months of the year. One month for each pomegranate seed. For the other six months of the year she will return to her mother."

Hades finally agreed to the plan. Within an hour Persephone, reunited with her mother, was blinking in the bright sunlight.

Now, when Persephone is with her mother the Earth is green and it is summer. When winter comes and the Earth is cold, Persephone is with her husband in his dark palace beneath the mountain.

BELLEROPHON AND THE FLYING HORSE

Once long ago a young man named Bellerophon was staying with the King of Argos. The king's wife was impressed by Bellerophon and said as much to her husband. She talked about him so much that the king grew tired of listening to her.

"All you talk about is Bellerophon," he grumbled. "Try to think about something different for a change. The boy is far too young to be a hero."

His foolish wife took no notice. Day after day she told the king how handsome Bellerophon was, how clever and how brave. At last the king grew so jealous that he decided to get rid of Bellerophon, but without telling his wife. He handed Bellerophon a sealed letter and asked him to deliver it to the King of Lycia.

"This is a most important letter," he told Bellerophon. "Be sure you give it to him."

Bellerophon agreed to deliver the letter and set off at once. He soon reached Lycia and met the king. The two of them got on well

15

right from the start. The king entertained him so lavishly that it was several days before Bellerophon remembered the letter.

"Forgive me, Your Majesty," he said. "I was asked to give you this." The king opened the letter. As he read it he turned quite pale.

"Whatever is the matter?" asked Bellerophon. "Is it bad news?" The king made no answer, but began to mutter to himself.

"This is treachery," he whispered. "I cannot believe it." Then he looked up at Bellerophon. "Never ask me about this letter," he commanded, and he threw it straight on the fire.

That night when Bellerophon went to bed he wondered about what was in the letter, but he was tired and soon fell asleep. The king, however, could not sleep. The letter had given him a terrible shock. It said that Bellerophon was a wicked young man and asked the king to have him killed.

"How could I do such a thing?" murmured the king. "Bellerophon seems such a pleasant young man, and he is a guest in my house. The King of Argos is known for his hot temper and he may soon regret this rash decision."

He paced up and down until at last he had an idea. "I shall send Bellerophon to slay the Chimaera," he decided. "He may well die in the attempt, but if he succeeds even the King of Argos will have to admit that he is a true hero."

So the next day the king told Bellerophon about the ferocious monster that was causing distress to the people of his kingdom and begged him to do something about it.

"The Chimaera is ruining their lives," said the king. "I implore you to destroy it for me. You will find it over in the hills where the sun rises."

Bellerophon was rather puzzled by all this, but he agreed to go.

16

He walked for many miles without seeing a sign of the monster and eventually stopped to ask an old farmer if he was going in the right direction. When Bellerophon mentioned what he was looking for the old man's eyes widened in alarm.

"Stay away from the Chimaera," he warned Bellerophon. "It's the vilest creature ever born. Plenty of young men have tried to kill it, but they have all died in the attempt."

"Perhaps I will have better luck," said Bellerophon hopefully. The old farmer shook his head.

"Young people today just will not listen to reason," he grumbled, "but if you are determined to get yourself killed, take that path through the woods. It will lead you to the Chimaera."

Bellerophon thanked the farmer politely and went on his way, trying not to be alarmed by what he had been told. He was not looking forward to fighting the Chimaera, but if he turned back without even trying he would be called a coward.

An hour later he sat down to rest, and to his astonishment a beautiful woman appeared before him.

"I am Athene, goddess of wisdom," she told him. "I know you plan to fight the Chimaera and I will help you." She held out a bridle and, as Bellerophon took it from her, she smiled at him and vanished.

"How odd," thought Bellerophon, staring at the bridle. "What possible use could a bridle be when I have no horse?" The bridle was of finest white leather studded with gold and decorated with precious jewels. "I shall take it with me," he said, and went on his way, puzzling over the strange gift. What Bellerophon did not notice was that far above him Pegasus, the winged horse of the gods, was wheeling and prancing among the clouds. Suddenly the snow white horse flew down to Earth to drink at a spring of pure water. Bellerophon was overjoyed when he saw the graceful creature before him. Now he knew why Athene had given him the bridle.

He approached the horse slowly, speaking softly to reassure him. "I know you are Pegasus," he said. "You are always ridden by the gods. I am not a god, but Athene has given me this bridle and I must ride you when I go to fight the dreadful Chimaera." Pegasus nodded his head as if he understood, but just as Bellerophon reached out to touch him, the horse sprang into the air and out of reach. For a moment Bellerophon thought the horse would fly away but then he came down again to drink. Eventually Bellerophon gave up his attempt to catch the horse. He put down the bridle and stood by, quietly observing. Pegasus was a fine animal with hoofs and wings of silver and a flowing mane and tail. Suddenly Bellerophon ran forward, jumped onto the horse's back and clung to his mane. The horse tried every trick he knew to throw off his unwanted rider. He flew up into the air and swooped down again, but somehow Bellerophon managed to stay on his back. At last Pegasus flew down to land beside the spring once more.

Bellerophon guessed that now Pegasus would wear the bridle and he slipped it over the horse's head. Then he sprang once more on to the horse's back. "Take me to the Chimaera!" he cried and Pegasus leapt upwards, tossing his head with excitement.

They flew for many miles until at last they came to a valley where the grass and trees were trampled and broken. Far below them a village lay in ruins. From the dark hills beyond the valley they heard a thunderous rumbling roar.

"That must be the Chimaera," whispered Bellerophon. He leant forward and reassuringly patted the horse's neck, but his own heart

beat faster at the thought of what was to come. Pegasus showed no fear, but flew on towards the rumbling sound. Soon they were confronted by a horrible sight. The Chimaera rose up before them; this was no ordinary beast – the monster had *three* heads!

One head roared – it was the head of a lion. The second head hissed – it was the head of a giant snake. The third and last head bleated like a goat and had two sharp horns.

Bellerophon was terrified. He almost wished he could turn back but then he remembered Athene. She had sent Pegasus to help him and that made Bellerophon feel much braver.

"Death to the cruel Chimaera!" he shouted and drew out his

sword. The lion's head reached out toward him, its mouth ready to swallow him up but the winged horse darted sideways and Bellerophon cut off the head with one mighty blow. The Chimaera's rage was frightful. The snake's head lunged at Bellerophon hissing loudly but down came the sword again. Chop! And away rolled the snake's head.

"Two heads gone and one to go!" shouted Bellerophon, but the Chimaera was not going to be beaten quite so easily. Without warning it reared up on its hind legs and reached out with its fearsome claws. They sank into the winged horse, who whinnied with pain. Silver feathers floated down and the beautiful white mane was suddenly speckled with blood.

The sight of the horse's blood made Bellerophon forget his own fear. Without a thought for his own safety he slashed again and again at the goat's head until that too lay bleeding on the ground. Now the Chimaera had lost all of its three heads and it collapsed in a heap.

Bellerophon waited, his sword at the ready, but the Chimaera would rise no more.

A great cry went up as the people ran from their hiding places in the ruined village. "The Chimaera is dead!" they cried, cheering and waving as Pegasus and Bellerophon flew skyward once more. They watched the young man and the horse as they rose higher and higher and disappeared at last among the rolling clouds.

The grateful people then set about rebuilding their village and replanting their crops. The memory of the beautiful white horse and its valiant rider would live on in their hearts for ever. Bellerophon had escaped death and no one could now doubt that he was indeed a hero.

ANDROMEDA AND THE SEA MONSTER

ONCE upon a time there was an Ethiopian king whose name was Cepheus. He had a wife, Cassiopeia, who was rather foolish. When their daughter was born, Cassiopeia thought she was the most wonderful baby there had ever been.

"Our little Andromeda is so good," she would say. "She never cries and she sleeps right through the night."

When Andromeda was a little older, Cassiopeia continued to tell everyone how wonderful she was.

"She's walking already," she cried, "and she is starting to talk."

Cassiopeia's friends grew very tired of hearing about Andromeda; they all believed their own children were more wonderful. One day, Cassiopeia went too far. On Andromeda's seventeenth birthday, her mother smiled at her proudly.

22

"You are more beautiful than the wood nymphs," she said, "and much more beautiful than the sea nymphs."

Unfortunately for Cassiopeia, Poseidon, the god of the sea, was listening. He lived in a palace far below the waves, where he ruled all the sea creatures, from the smallest fish to the largest whale.

"Foolish woman!" he roared, "How dare you! My nymphs are easily more beautiful than any mortal princess. I shall teach you a lesson you will not forget in a hurry."

He rose from the middle of the deepest ocean and blew the surface of the water into huge waves. These waves rolled across the seas and crashed against the shores of Ethiopia. They broke with such force that the very cliffs trembled. Boats moored along the coast were smashed to pieces and many poor sailors lost their lives. Then Poseidon sent a tidal wave sweeping inland. It moved at such a pace that it carried away houses and bridges and many more innocent people died. When the king heard what had happened he went at once to see the terrible destruction for himself.

"This is a catastrophe!" he cried. "Poseidon's power is terrible. How can we stop it?"

He went to the top of a cliff and called out to the god of the sea. Eventually Poseidon appeared from the centre of a whirlpool.

"Spare us, Poseidon!" cried Cepheus. "My wife is foolish, but she did not mean to offend you. Forgive us and we will do anything you ask. We will give you gold or jewels – anything you want – only do not destroy my kingdom with your mighty waves."

Poseidon made no answer but waved his hand, and at once hundreds of sea nymphs rose from the sea around him. They were strange but beautiful creatures – half-human, half-fish.

23

"What do you think of my sea nymphs?" Poseidon demanded.
"Are they not more beautiful than any mortals?"

The king hesitated – he knew his wife was listening.

"Well?" roared Poseidon.

"I think...," began Cepheus, "at least I mean..." Poseidon did not give him a second chance. His eyes grew dark and his voice shook with rage. The sea nymphs dived beneath the waves in alarm.

"You offer me anything I want?" cried Poseidon. "Very well. I want your daughter. She must be sacrificed to save your kingdom."

The king turned pale and a gasp of horror went up from the watching crowd. Then Poseidon told the king to tie his daughter to a rock on the sea shore.

"I shall send my largest sea monster to devour her," he said. Then with a cruel laugh, the sea god sank beneath the waves and the swirling water closed over his head.

The people of Ethiopia were dismayed and the king and queen quite distraught. Cassiopeia begged her husband not to sacrifice their daughter.

"It is all my fault," she wept. "My stupid boasting has caused all this trouble."

The king did not know what to say, but Andromeda stepped forward and spoke up bravely.

"You must do as Poseidon says," she told him. "The people must not suffer any more. We have offended the god of the sea and it is right that I should die."

At first the king protested, but at last he had to admit that there was nothing else to be done. Andromeda was led down to the beach and tied to a huge rock at the bottom of the cliff. There she was left to await her fate.

The daylight faded into night, and night gave way to dawn before the sea monster appeared. The waves parted to reveal a huge, shapeless head, two tiny eyes that glittered with malice, an ugly beak-like mouth and countless writhing tentacles.

As the horrifying creature moved towards her, Andromeda

closed her eyes and prayed for courage. Suddenly there was a cry from the air above her and, to her astonishment, she saw a young man flying towards her. He wore a dark helmet and carried a strangely curved sword. The sun was behind him and the sea monster did not see him as he swept down. He was only just in time, for the monster was already crawling out of the sea when the young man struck the first blow. The battle was fierce, but it did not last long because the man was a favourite of the gods and they helped him to overcome the monster.

When at last the sea monster lay dead upon the sands, the young man untied the rope that bound Andromeda to the rock. He told her his name was Perseus. She told him her story and he was astonished by her bravery. By this time the people were flocking down to the sea shore to see what had happened. They were amazed to see the monster lying dead and they all wanted to congratulate Perseus and shake his hand.

The king and queen thanked Perseus for saving Andromeda's life and for ridding their kingdom of the monster.

"I will make you the richest man in the kingdom," the king told Perseus. But the young man did not ask for riches. Instead he asked for Andromeda's hand in marriage, for the two young people had fallen in love. The king gladly granted the request and very soon, amid great rejoicing, Andromeda and Perseus were married.

KING MIDAS
AND
THE
GOLDEN TOUCH

MANY years ago in the land of Lydia there was a beautiful garden. Roses of every shade grew there and on warm summer nights the air was heavy with their fragrance. The garden belonged to a palace and the palace was the home of a king, whose name was Midas. He was, it is true, rather greedy but on the whole no better and no worse than any other man. Midas had a loving wife and a daughter whom he adored, but he was still discontented. He wanted to be the most powerful king in the world; he wanted everyone to envy him.

One day, as he was walking through the palace garden, he was startled to see a pair of legs sticking out from beneath his favourite rose bush. The strange thing about these legs was that they had hoofs instead of feet. The king stared at them for a moment and then called for the gardener's boy.

"What do you make of that?" he asked. The boy parted the branches of the rose bush and peered through.

"It's a satyr, Your Majesty," he reported, trying not to laugh. "I think it's Silenus."

The satyrs were strange, mischievous creatures – half man, half beast – who roamed the world in search of adventure. Midas frowned, angry that somebody should be sleeping in his garden.

The boy ran off to fetch the gardener and between them they dragged Silenus from under the rose bush and pulled him to his feet. Silenus grinned foolishly. He was holding an empty wine jar.

"You are trespassing in my garden," Midas told him severely. "What have you to say for yourself?" The old satyr shrugged.

"I got lost, so I sat down for a drink," he told the king, looking quite unrepentant.

"Disgraceful," said Midas. "I shall send word to your master at once." Silenus began to look worried, for his master was the god Dionysus who was not only powerful but also quick tempered.

"I beg you not to do that," he cried. "He will be angry with me. Suppose I make a bargain with you? If you will overlook my foolishness I will entertain you with strange and wonderful tales, better than any you have heard before."

Midas agreed and the satyr stayed on in the palace delighting the king with wonderful accounts of his adventures. At the end of the week Midas sent the satyr back to Dionysus. The god was very fond of Silenus, despite his many faults, and was pleased to see him safe and sound. He wanted to thank Midas for taking care of the old satyr and offered the king any gift he cared to name.

Any gift he cared to name! What a marvellous opportunity! He pondered for a whole day and a night and then asked Dionysus if he could make a wish. The god agreed and Midas asked for the power to turn whatever he touched into gold. The god granted his wish and Midas was jubilant.

"Imagine a king with a golden touch!" he cried. "I shall be the wealthiest and most powerful king in the world."

The king began to experiment with his new gift. He hurried into the garden and touched one of the flowers. At once, the whole bush turned to gold. He went from bush to bush, touching all the blooms, until the entire garden had turned to gold. Then he looked around him. Suddenly Midas felt doubtful. Gone were the colours and the glorious perfume. The garden was still and lifeless.

Inside the palace, the king called for a goblet of wine. As soon as it touched his lips the wine turned to gold and he could not drink.

A terrible thought occurred to him.

"What will happen when I eat?" he wondered. With trembling fingers he reached out to take an apple from a bowl of fruit. As soon as he touched it the apple turned to gold.

"What have I done?" he whispered. "If I cannot eat or drink I shall die!" He knew that he had made a terrible mistake and decided to beg Dionysus to take back his gift. "I will go to him at once," he cried; but his decision came too late. At that very moment his daughter ran into the room.

"Stay away from me!" Midas shouted, but she took no notice. She threw her arms around him – and was turned to gold. His daughter was now a gleaming but lifeless statue. The king stared at her in horror.

"What have I done to you?" he cried, kneeling beside her. His grief was so great that nobody could console him. He hurried to the palace of Dionysus and threw himself at the god's feet.

"Forgive my stupid greed!" he begged. "Tell me what I must do to save my child. I will do anything you say."

Dionysus told him to find the river Pactolus and wash himself in its waters. Midas set off at once. He went alone, and walked for many miles over rough and stony ground.

When he reached the river he found it flowing deep and strong. Midas waded straight in. He was instantly swept away by the current. When at last he managed to reach the shore, he wondered if the curse had indeed been washed from him. Looking back he saw that the river now gleamed and sparkled in the sun. On the river bed tiny nuggets of gold lay among the pebbles. Dionysus had spoken truthfully and the terrible power had left him. Joyfully Midas made his way home.

As he approached the palace, Midas' daughter ran to greet him. He lifted her into his arms and carried her into the garden. Midas was overjoyed to hear her laughter once again and he sighed happily as he breathed in the fragrance of the flowers.

"I have learnt my lesson," he said softly, "and I am content."

ATALANTA

One day, many years ago, a king was waiting for his child to be born. The king, whose name was Iasus, had no time for girls.

"Who wants girls?" he would ask. "They are hopeless at fighting and no good at hunting."

It never crossed the king's mind that his wife would have a baby girl. When he heard the child's first cry he jumped for joy.

"My son is born," he cried. "How pleased the people will be when they hear the news! They will sing and dance in the streets."

Just then one of the queen's attendants appeared.

"Well?" shouted the king. "Don't stand there staring, woman. Tell me the good news."

The attendant looked frightened.

"Your Majesty, the queen has given you a beautiful baby girl. Her name is Atalanta."

At first the king could not believe his ears. Then he *would* not believe his ears. Then he flew into a terrible rage.

"Take the child away!" he shouted. "The people do not want a princess, and neither do I!"

The queen sobbed bitterly and begged the king to be reasonable.

"Only look at your daughter," she cried, "and you will change your mind."

But the king was so disappointed that he would not even glance at her. He told his soldiers to take the baby into the mountains and leave her there.

The baby was still sleeping peacefully when the soldiers pushed her into a cave. When she woke up she was hungry and began to cry for her mother. Now further back in the cave was a she-bear and her cubs. The bear heard the child crying and thought she was another bear cub, so she brought her up with her own young. This is how Atalanta learnt the ways of the wild creatures. The bear

taught her to search for berries and to hunt for fish in the streams. Later Artemis, the goddess of hunting, took care of the young girl and taught her to be a better hunter than any man. She could run faster too. With her bare feet and clothes made of animal skins, no one could have guessed that she was of royal birth.

One day news reached Atalanta of a ferocious wild boar that was causing havoc in the kingdom of Calydon. It was the largest boar ever seen and was bringing great misery to everyone. It trampled down the crops and killed and injured people. The Prince of Calydon, who was called Meleager, decided to rid the land of the terrible boar. He knew that he could never succeed on his own. He decided to organize a boar hunt and sent out notices inviting people to take part. He promised the boar's head as a reward to the bravest hunter. Now as soon as Atalanta heard about the hunting party she set off to join it. When she reached Calydon, she came across the band of hunters who were about to go in search of the boar. She asked if she could join them, but the young men only laughed at her.

"Whoever heard of a woman hunting a boar?" jeered one of them. "Go home and bake a pie. You have no business with us."

But Meleager shook his head. He had fallen in love with Atalanta.

"I say she shall join us," he said. "She has a bow and a quiver full of arrows. She shall come along with us and then we shall see how well she hunts." The others grumbled but Meleager took no notice and finally they all set off in search of the ferocious beast.

They followed the boar's tracks for many miles and they eventually caught up with it in a clearing in the forest. It was even bigger and more terrifying than they had expected. Before the men had a chance to plan their attack, the savage animal gave a furious roar and charged towards them. Within seconds one of them lay dead, trampled by the boar which then disappeared into the trees. Meleager shouted a warning as the boar turned and came heading towards them again, snorting horribly and pawing the ground. There followed a fierce and bloody battle and in the confusion a spear meant for the boar killed another hunter. The men shouted wildly at each other. Only Atalanta remained quite calm. She knelt down, fitted an arrow to her bow and waited. When the animal caught sight of her, he lowered his huge head and raced towards her. Atalanta's arrow sped straight and true and sank into the boar's neck. The boar fell to the ground, but it was not quite dead. Meleager finished it off with a blow from his sword.

Atalanta had proved that she could hunt as well as the men – and they were not at all pleased. They turned away from her without a word of praise, and one of them congratulated the prince instead, saying "Well done Meleager. You have killed the boar."

Meleager was ashamed of them all. "I salute you!" he cried. "You struck the first blow. You are indeed a worthy hunter."

Still the men muttered among themselves. "Women should stay at home," grumbled one of them.

Atalanta merely smiled, but Meleager was determined to show her that he, at least, appreciated what she had done. He cut off the boar's head and offered it to her as a prize.

"You deserve it more than any of us," he declared loudly.

Atalanta thanked him, but said that she did not want the boar's head. She started to walk away, but Meleager followed her.

"Wait! Please wait!" As Atalanta turned back, he told her that he

wanted to marry her. "I have fallen in love with you," he said, "and I want to make you Princess of Calydon."

Atalanta shook her head. "I'm afraid I would not make a very good wife," she said kindly. "I am too used to my wild and lonely life. I would not be happy any other way. But I thank you for your kindness to me today and I shall never forget you."

As she walked away through the trees, her hair glinting in the sunlight, Meleager sighed deeply. "Goodbye," he called softly, full of admiration for the brave young woman who had proved herself to be his equal.

It was not long before news reached Iasus of his daughter's success. He had to admit that he had made a great mistake and begged Atalanta to forgive him, which she did gladly. And so, at long last, the family was reunited.

PYGMALION'S STATUE

Many years ago, on the island of Cyprus, lived a king called Pygmalion. Although he was king, Pygmalion was a quiet man. He was unmarried and had few friends. Pygmalion felt no need for friends because he spent all his time making statues. People came from miles around to see the beautiful statues he made, but Pygmalion never sold them. He was so rich that he did not need to earn his living like ordinary men and women. Instead he gave the statues to Aphrodite, the goddess of love, and they were used to decorate her temples.

Pygmalion's old nurse worried about him.

"I wish you would find yourself a wife," she told him. "I shall not live for ever, and who will look after you when I am gone? It's not natural for a king to live on his own. You must marry and have a son. Otherwise, who is to rule after you?"

Pygmalion smiled at her.

"When I find a woman as beautiful as one of my statues I shall marry her," he promised. The old nurse sighed. She suggested various women who might make a good wife for him, but Pygmalion rejected them all, saying "They are all greedy and cruel. I pity the men who have such women for their wives."

The old nurse gave up in despair. She had looked after Pygmalion since he was a boy and knew how stubborn he could be.

Several days later Pygmalion decided to make a new statue. He would create a beautiful woman out of the finest marble he could buy. As soon as he started it he knew that it would be the best statue he had ever made. Day and night he worked feverishly, unable to think of anything else.

"You must eat," begged his old nurse.

"Later," said Pygmalion.

"You must sleep," she insisted.

The king took no notice at all.

He worked for nearly a month and then it was finished. As Pygmalion gazed at the white marble statue, the beautiful face seemed to smile back at him. She was so lifelike that even Pygmalion was astounded.

"How did I create such beauty?" he whispered to himself. "Aphrodite must have inspired me." The old nurse came into the workroom and she, too, was astonished by Pygmalion's creation.

"It looks so real," she gasped. "I can't help thinking she will speak to us at any moment. It's certainly your finest work, and will look very good in Aphrodite's temple."

Slowly Pygmalion turned to her. "No," he said. "This statue will not go to the temple. I shall keep it here with me for ever."

As the days went by Pygmalion grew very fond of his statue. He began to talk to it as though it were alive and began to think of it as his wife. He even gave the statue a name – he called it Galatea.

He realized that he was falling in love with his own creation but still he would not give it up.

"I shall go to Aphrodite," he told himself. "I shall tell her about Galatea and ask her to help me. I have served Aphrodite well all my life. I know she will not fail me."

He went straight to the temple and knelt down.

"Take pity on me, goddess," he begged. "I truly love Galatea and

if I cannot have her for my wife I shall go to my grave a lonely man, for I shall never love anyone else.''

After a moment he became strangely weary and fell asleep. He had a dream in which he heard the sweet voice of Aphrodite.

''You are a good man, Pygmalion,'' she told him. ''Go home and claim your bride.'' Pygmalion opened his eyes and looked around him, but he was alone in the temple.

''Did I dream all that?'' he wondered. ''Or did Aphrodite herself really speak to me?''

Full of hope he left the temple and hurried back to the palace. He went straight to his workroom and stood before the statue.

''Galatea,'' he said, ''I claim you as my bride.'' He put his arms around the marble body and kissed the cold, beautiful lips. At once the cold marble grew warm and colour flowed over it. He saw that her hair was the colour of ripe corn and her eyes were as blue as the deepest ocean. Then she spoke to him.

''Dear Pygmalion, I shall be a good and faithful wife to you,'' she promised, ''and I shall give you a son to rule after you.''

The people of Cyprus were overjoyed at the news of their king's marriage. There were celebrations all over the island in honour of their wedding. True to her words, the following year Galatea had a baby son, whom they called Paphos. As the old nurse took the baby in her arms, there were tears of joy in her eyes.

''Now I can die in peace,'' she said. ''Pygmalion is a happy man.''

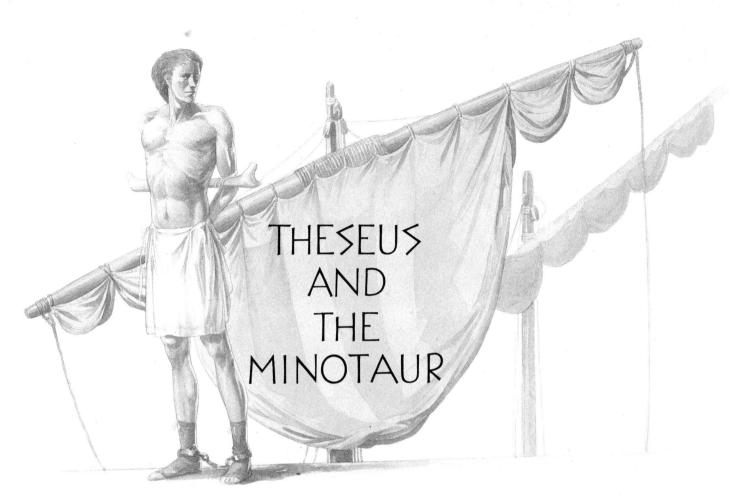

THESEUS AND THE MINOTAUR

THERE was once a very powerful king, called Minos, who ruled over the island of Crete. He waged war upon the King of Athens, whose name was Aegeus. When the war was over, Minos was victorious. He told the Athenian king that every year he must send seven young men and seven girls to his island to be fed to the minotaur. This was a dreadful blow to the defeated Athenians, for the minotaur was a terrible beast, with the body of a man and the head of a bull. The minotaur lived below the king's palace in a bewildering maze of passages which was called a labyrinth. Nobody who had been sent into the labyrinth had ever found the way out.

Now Aegeus had a son called Theseus, who was a very brave young prince. When he heard what Minos was demanding he said, "I shall go to Crete as one of the seven young men and somehow I shall try to kill the minotaur." His father was horrified at the idea, but Theseus insisted and soon his ship set sail.

When the Athenians reached Crete, crowds gathered at the water's edge to see the ship, watching silently as the anchor splashed into the sea and the prisoners were rowed ashore. One of the onlookers was particularly upset at the sight; this was Ariadne, the daughter of King Minos. She caught sight of one of the prisoners – an intelligent-looking man with brown eyes and dark, curly hair. Instantly she fell in love with him, not knowing that he was the son of the King of Athens. Ariadne made up her mind to save this prisoner from his dreadful fate.

"Whatever can I do?" she wondered desperately.

She realized that the only person who could help her was a man called Daedalus; it was he who had designed and built the labyrinth. She ran all the way back to the palace and found Daedalus in the garden. She told him how unhappy she was about the young Athenian and begged him to help her. To her surprise he took a ball of thread from his pocket and pressed it into her hand.

"A ball of thread," she cried. "What on earth am I to do with this?" Daedalus glanced around to see that no one could hear them.

"You will know when the time comes," he whispered, and would say no more. Later that night she crept down to the prison with a jar of wine.

"Drink this," she told the guards, "and look the other way while I speak to the prisoners." The guards agreed cheerfully and allowed her into the prison. She told the Athenians that she was the daughter of King Minos. "I don't want you to die," she said. "I wish I could help you."

Then Theseus stepped forward. "My father is Aegeus, King of Athens," he said. "I will go into the labyrinth and try to kill the minotaur. But if I succeed, how am I to find my way out again?"

Ariadne remembered the ball of thread Daedalus had given her;

45

it was still in her pocket. She gave it to him at once. "Tie it to the inside of the gate when you enter the labyrinth," she told him. "Unwind it as you go through the passages. If you do kill the minotaur you can wind it back and find your way out."

Theseus thanked her, but then he frowned. "Suppose your father finds out that you have helped us?" he asked. "He will be very angry. Perhaps you should come back to Athens with us if we are fortunate enough to escape."

Ariadne agreed and then she hurried back to the palace. The next day all went as planned and when Theseus was pushed into the labyrinth he had the ball of thread safely hidden in his sleeve. He tied the end to the inside of the gate and began to make his way through the gloomy passages. He turned a corner and then another corner and then another. He knew that without the ball of thread he would be hopelessly lost. Round and round he went until at last he heard a deep roaring and guessed that the minotaur could not be far away. At last he came face to face with the hideous creature. The minotaur's body was covered with hair and his bull's head was large and ferocious. Two red eyes gleamed wickedly below the curved horns. Theseus had only seconds in which to decide how best to attack the minotaur. As it ran towards him he noticed that the heavy bull's head was balanced on a thin man's neck. That would be the weakest part.

Theseus leapt forward and clasped the minotaur around the neck and squeezed as hard as he could. It struggled wildly and for some time they wrestled to and fro. Then at last the minotaur stumbled and fell to the ground. Theseus stared down in disbelief. Had he really killed the minotaur? He half expected the creature to leap to his feet again but nothing happened. It really was dead and the prisoners from Athens were safe.

With a sigh of relief Theseus turned away and began to wind back the thread. It led him safely to the gateway where Ariadne was waiting. Together they hurried to the prison and released the rest of the Athenian prisoners.

"The minotaur is dead," he told them and a great cheer went up. Theseus thanked Ariadne with a kiss and they ran down to the beach to rejoin the waiting ship. Theseus had killed the minotaur and they believed their troubles were over. King Minos, however, did not want his daughter to go to Athens with Theseus. He ordered his ships to sail after them and bring her back. But that was not to be, for the Athenian sailors had not been idle. They had made holes in the ships of Minos' fleet and they soon began to sink. The king could only watch helplessly as the Athenian ship sailed away and disappeared over the horizon. Minos had won a war, but he had lost a daughter!

DAEDALUS AND ICARUS

DAEDALUS was a very clever man who worked for Minos, King of Crete. It was Daedalus who designed the labyrinth, a maze which was famous because no one could escape from it. But one day the princess Ariadne asked Daedalus to help a prisoner escape from the labyrinth, and this Daedalus did. He knew that the king would be furious when he heard. Poor Daedalus was a frightened man.

"He will blame me for everything," he told his son, "and he will certainly kill me."

His son, whose name was Icarus, was also frightened. "If the king is angry with you," he said, "he will also be angry with me because I am your son."

Daedalus put his hand on his son's shoulder. "I am sorry that I brought all this trouble upon us," he said.

49

The king made enquiries and soon found out that Daedalus had helped the young man escape from the labyrinth. He was beside himself with rage, and made up his mind to punish both father and son. He could not think of a harsh enough punishment so he decided to kill them.

"I told Daedalus to build a maze from which *no one* could escape," he roared. "He has made me look a fool in the eyes of the people."

Minos sent his soldiers to arrest Daedalus and Icarus, but they were hiding in a cave and could not be found. The king did not let this worry him. He knew that Crete was an island and that Daedalus and his son could only escape by sea. That meant asking the help of a fisherman. The king made it quite clear that anyone who helped them to escape would be killed.

"I can wait," he said. "They will never get away by boat and they cannot fly."

He could not know that even as he spoke Daedalus was designing a pair of wings! He built a light wooden frame and covered it with wax. Into the wax he stuck thousands of feathers. His son watched with growing amazement. When they were finished Daedalus said "See! The wings of a bird! Now we can fly to Athens where we will be safe from the king."

When both pairs of wings were ready they strapped them on. Icarus knew how clever his father was and he did not doubt that the wings would carry them safely to Athens.

"We will go after dark," said Daedalus, "and I will lead the way. If by any chance we get separated, fly on alone and we will meet up in Athens. And remember, come as quickly as you can and do not fly too high!"

As soon as it was dark Daedalus and Icarus went to the top of a cliff, making sure that nobody saw them. They flapped their wings and found themselves soaring up into the darkness. It was a wonderful sensation. Daedalus flew steadily on towards Athens, but after a while Icarus began to enjoy himself and forgot his father's warning. He felt like a bird – like an enormous seagull – and wanted to try out his wings. He began to wheel and circle and swoop through the cold air. "How graceful I am," he said to himself. Icarus thought he could easily catch up with his father, but when eventually he began to look for him, Daedalus was nowhere to be found. Icarus began to feel rather worried. Where exactly was his father, he wondered. And which way was the right way to go? It would be terrible if he went the wrong way and found himself back in Crete. He decided to fly just a little higher to see if he could find his father. Daedalus had warned him not to go too high, but Icarus thought he would have to take a chance. Up and up he went, but there was no sign of Daedalus and poor Icarus began to panic. Soon it would be morning. Someone might see him and think he was a bird. They might try to shoot him down with a well-aimed arrow! He shuddered at the thought of it.

He decided to fly a little higher, but by this time the sun was rising in the East. He flew on. The warm rays of the sun shone on to the wings and the wax began to melt. Icarus did not realize what was happening at first, but suddenly he looked down and saw a few feathers floating below him. He thought they must have come from a bird, but there were no birds in sight. He could feel himself losing height. He flapped his wings faster and more feathers floated down. With a cry of horror Icarus looked at his wings and saw that they were falling apart. Too late he remembered his father's warning. Too late he understood the reason for it.

"Father!" he screamed, but his cry just echoed in the empty sky. No answer came. "Father! Save me!" he cried, but his father was by now in Athens, many miles away. Icarus fell down, down, down, into the sea and was drowned. Poor Daedalus, hoping against hope, waited in vain for the son who would never join him.

JASON AND THE GOLDEN FLEECE

THERE was once a young prince whose name was Jason. He grew up in a cave in the mountains with a centaur – a wise and kindly creature that was half-man, half-horse. When Jason was nearly twenty he wanted to know why he was living in a cave if he was really a prince.

The centaur explained, "Your uncle Pelias made himself king just before you were born, and put your father, King Aeson, in prison. Your father saw to it that you were brought here for safekeeping." Jason was very angry when he heard this.

"I will rescue my father," he cried, "and make him king again."

The centaur shook his head. "No," he said. "Your father is too old to be king now and so is your uncle. But go to Pelias and tell him who you are. Ask him to give you the kingdom which is rightfully yours. You are a grown man and the people of the kingdom will welcome a new, young king."

So Jason went to his uncle who agreed to give up the throne, but on one condition. Jason was to prove his bravery by going to fetch the Golden Fleece. Only when he had done this would Pelias give up his kingdom.

The fleece had once belonged to a beautiful golden ram. The ram was such a rare creature that after its death the fleece was taken and hung in a temple for all the world to see. Because it was so valuable the king was afraid that somebody would steal it, so he set a fearsome dragon to guard it – a dragon that never slept. Everybody knew that to steal the Golden Fleece was an impossible and dangerous task.

Jason chose his ship and called it the Argo. He also chose his crew from some of the bravest men he could find. These men were known as the Argonauts. They set sail and started on their long and dangerous journey to find the Golden Fleece. On their way they had many adventures, but eventually they came in sight of their destination. A great cry went up from the weary sailors. But Jason knew that for him the worst part of the adventure was still to come.

"Wait for me here," he told the Argonauts. "I must present myself to the king." The Argonauts wished Jason good luck; they knew he would not return home without the Golden Fleece.

When Jason reached the palace, the first person he met was Medea, the king's daughter. She was very beautiful and people whispered that she had magic powers. She took one look at the handsome stranger and fell in love with him.

"My father will not want to give up the Golden Fleece," she told him, "but I may be able to help you. If I do, I shall ask for something in return."

"If it is within my power you shall have it," Jason replied rather rashly. Medea smiled.

"I want to go back to Greece with you as your wife," she told him. Now Jason was determined to take back the Golden Fleece, so he agreed to Medea's suggestion. Medea took him to her father and the young man explained the reason for his visit.

"I may be willing to part with the fleece," the king said, "but if you are to take it you must prove that you are worthy of it. This is the task I shall set you. First you must catch and tame two wild bulls. Then you must yoke them to a plough and plant a field with dragons' teeth. If you are still alive after this, come back to me."

Medea took Jason to one side. "It is certain death," she told him. "The bulls have fiery breath and burn up all those who approach them. But I may be able to help you."

She gave him a magic lotion to rub into his skin and told him that it would save him from the bulls' fiery breath.

The next day, protected by Medea's magic lotion, Jason

managed to capture the two wild bulls and then he yoked them to a plough. The bulls were very angry and difficult to handle, but after a long struggle the field was ploughed and ready for planting. Although Jason was exhausted he would not give in. He planted row upon row of dragons' teeth. By the time he had finished it was nearly dark.

"Now I have proved that I am brave," he told Medea. Medea smiled and pointed to the field. There the dragons' teeth were starting to grow!

"What is happening?" cried Jason.

Then, to his horror, he saw that the dragons' teeth were growing

into armed soldiers! They sprang up from the newly ploughed earth and their bright swords glistened in the setting sun.

Jason had no weapons. How could he defend himself? In alarm, he snatched up handfuls of earth and stones and flung them at the advancing army. Luck was on his side. In the failing light the soldiers could not see which direction the stones were coming from, and the fine dust blew into their eyes and half blinded them. They were so confused that they began to strike out in all directions and ended up fighting each other! Medea and Jason watched in awe as the battle raged on. It did not end until all the soldiers lay dead upon the ground.

King Aites soon learnt that Jason had carried out the task he had set him. He realized that Medea must have helped him and was beside himself with rage.

"You shall never marry my daughter," he told Jason. "Leave my kingdom at once, and go back to Greece where you belong. You and your Argonauts are not welcome here."

It was Medea's turn to be angry. She had made up her mind that she would marry Jason, so she decided to help him once more. That night she led Jason by a secret path to the temple where the Golden Fleece hung between two pillars. It gleamed in the moonlight and Jason caught his breath in wonder.

"It is more beautiful than I ever dreamt!" he exclaimed, and he was more determined than ever to take it back to Greece with him. But between Jason and the fleece lay the fearsome dragon that never slept. Its eyes were alert and watchful; flames and smoke poured from its nostrils. Medea was not going to let Jason risk his life again, so she gave him a small bottle filled with blue liquid.

"Take this," she told Jason. "The dragon always drinks from that pool beside the temple. Tip this magic potion into the pool and

when he drinks it will send him to sleep, but only for a minute. You will have to snatch the fleece and run like the wind. I will wait for you on the beach with the Argonauts. But remember – you will only have a minute before the dragon wakes up again.''

Jason thanked her. When she had gone he crept round the pool and tipped in the blue liquid. Then he hid behind the trees and waited for the dragon to feel thirsty. The pool was a short distance from the Golden Fleece, so Jason knew he dare not stumble or fall or else the dragon would be upon him. An hour passed and then the dragon lumbered to its feet and sniffed the air. It began to move towards the pool and Jason held his breath. The dragon took a few mouthfuls of water and then collapsed in a deep sleep. Jason raced forward and tugged at the Golden Fleece. It fell into his arms. He turned to make his escape. The fleece was much heavier than he expected and he stumbled over it. Then he ran as fast as he could. A minute passed and Jason heard the terrible dragon waking up. When the dragon saw that the Golden Fleece had gone he gave a mighty roar which instantly woke the king.

Jason reached the beach where Medea and the Argonauts were waiting and as soon as they were all on board they prepared to leave. Someone had told the king that Medea was on the Argo with Jason. Aites dashed to the beach, fuming with anger, and ordered a boat to go after them. Fortunately for Jason, the Argo had a good start on their pursuers and the king's boat could not catch up with them. With the beautiful Golden Fleece safely on board Jason started back to the country which he could now claim as his own.

THE GREEK GODS

Here is a list of gods mentioned in the stories. You may like to look out for them in anything else you read:

ZEUS was the King of the gods. His brothers were Poseidon and Hades. Zeus was the god of the earth and the sky. To show that he ruled the winds and rain, Zeus usually carried a thunderbolt in his right hand. In his left hand he carried a sceptre. An eagle often sat at his feet.

DEMETER was the sister of Zeus. She was known as the corn goddess because she helped the wheat and barley to grow and ripen. She wore a crown made of corn. She was Persephone's mother and was called the Earth-mother. People who worshipped Demeter built temples for her in the forests.

APHRODITE, the goddess of love, was a figure of charm, grace and beauty. People believed that she was the daughter of Zeus. She was also the goddess of gardens – the rose and the pomegranate remind us of her – and of animals, especially doves, sparrows and swans.

POSEIDON once had the power to create earthquakes but later he became god of the seas. With a trident in his hand, he would rise up through the waves. All the creatures of the sea were under his command. He was sometimes shown with the tail of a fish.

ATHENE, the daughter of Zeus, was born fully formed from Zeus's forehead, armed with spear, helmet and shield. She was the goddess of victory, wisdom and courage, and her emblem was a wise owl. She also carried an olive branch to show that she was the goddess of peace. The city of Athens is named after her.

HADES, King of the Underworld, was disliked by the other gods and feared by mortal men and women. When people died, their souls were carried down into Hades' underground kingdom where a terrible three-headed dog, Cerberus, guarded the gate so that they could never escape.

DIONYSUS, the son of Zeus, was the god of wine and merrymaking. He was brought up by nymphs on a mountainside. His followers were satyrs (half-men, half-horses). Sometimes he carried a goblet of wine, sometimes a staff entwined with vine leaves.

ARTEMIS, the goddess of hunting, was greatly skilled with a bow and arrow. She loved to hunt in the forests with a faithful hound beside her. She was also often seen with a tame deer and even a she-bear. Her friends were the nymphs who lived in the woods and mountains.